A Sunny Sunday Drive

Farmer Claude and Farmer Maude
went for a Sunday drive.
Farmer Claude and Farmer Maude
sat in the front of the truck.

The dog, the goat, the rooster, and pig came on their Sunday drive.

The dog, the goat, the rooster, and pig sat in the back of the truck.

"Which way should we go?"

cried Farmer Claude.

"Follow the sun!"

cried Farmer Maude.

They drove their truck up the hills

and down the hills

and along the sunny track.

Farmer Claude and Farmer Maude
went thumpity-jumpity-bump.

The dog, the goat, the rooster, and pig

went humpity-lumpity-clump.

Farmer Claude and Farmer Maude
didn't look left and didn't look right.
Farmer Claude and Farmer Maude
looked at the track ahead.

"Why don't you look behind you?"

the shaken animals said.

But Farmer Claude and Farmer Maude
couldn't hear the animals say:
"Rain, rain, go away.
Come again another day!"

Farmer Claude and Farmer Maude
didn't look left and didn't look right.
Farmer Claude and Farmer Maude
looked at the track ahead.

"Why don't you look behind you?"

the shivering animals said.

But Farmer Claude and Farmer Maude
couldn't hear the animals say:
"Wind, wind, go away.
Come again another day!"

Farmer Claude and Farmer Maude
looked at the sky ahead.
"This is a perfect Sunday drive.
It's very mild," they said.

The dog, the goat, the rooster, and pig

looked at the sky behind.

"This is an awful Sunday drive.

It's very wild," they whined.

Then Farmer Claude and Farmer Maude
turned and drove right back.
Down the hills and up the hills
and along the sunny track.

"That sunny Sunday drive was fun," they said. "We're lucky it was fine."

The animals just drooped and dripped
and then began to whine.

"That sunny Sunday drive," they said,

"was very far from FINE!"